Pops 5

Wise Publications
London/New York/Paris/Sydney/Copenhagen/Madrid/Tokyo

Exclusive Distributors:
Music Sales Limited
8/9 Frith Street, London W1D 3JB, England.
Music Sales Pty Limited
120 Rothschild Avenue, Rosebery, NSW 2018, Australia.

Order No. AM963248
ISBN 0-7119-8084-5
This book © Copyright 2001 by Wise Publications

Compiled by Nick Crispin
Music arranged by Stephen Duro
Music processed by Allegro Reproductions
Cover photograph (Travis) courtesy of London Features International

Printed in the United Kingdom by
Printwise (Haverhill) Limited, Haverhill, Suffolk.

Your Guarantee of Quality
As publishers, we strive to produce every book to the highest commercial standards.
The music has been freshly engraved and the book has been carefully designed to minimise
awkward page turns and to make playing from it a real pleasure.
Particular care has been given to specifying acid-free, neutral-sized paper made from pulps
which have not been elemental chlorine bleached. This pulp is from farmed sustainable forests
and was produced with special regard for the environment.
Throughout, the printing and binding have been planned to ensure a sturdy, attractive publication
which should give years of enjoyment.
If your copy fails to meet our high standards, please inform us and we will gladly replace it.

Music Sales' complete catalogue describes thousands of titles and is available in full colour sections
by subject, direct from Music Sales Limited. Please state your areas of interest
and send a cheque/postal order for £1.50 for postage to:
Music Sales Limited, Newmarket Road, Bury St. Edmunds, Suffolk IP33 3YB.

www.musicsales.com

Don't Stop Movin' - *S Club 7* 4

Eternity - *Robbie Williams*   10

Have A Nice Day - *Stereophonics*   15

Out Of Reach - *Gabrielle*   20

Pure And Simple - *Hear'Say*   25

Sing - *Travis* 44

This Year's Love - *David Gray*   30

What Took You So Long? - *Emma Bunton*   34

Whole Again - *Atomic Kitten*   40

Don't Stop Movin'

Words & Music by Simon Ellis, Sheppard Solomon & S Club 7

Moderately

Don't stop mov-in' to the fun-ky, fun-ky beat. Don't stop mov-in' to the

fun-ky, fun-ky beat. Yeah, oh come on! Don't stop mov-in' to the fun-ky, fun-ky beat.

Don't stop mov-in' to the S. Club beat. 1. (M) D. J. got the par-ty start-ed,

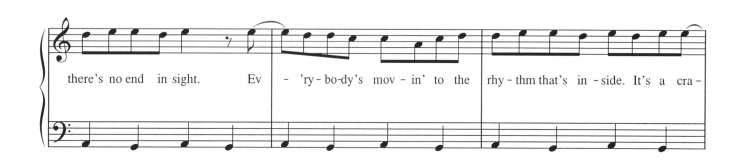

there's no end in sight. Ev-'ry-bo-dy's mov-in' to the rhy-thm that's in-side. It's a cra-

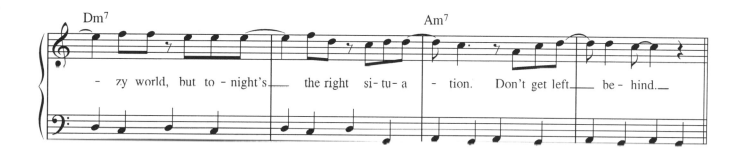

- zy world, but to - night's___ the right si - tu - a ___ - tion. Don't get left___ be - hind.___

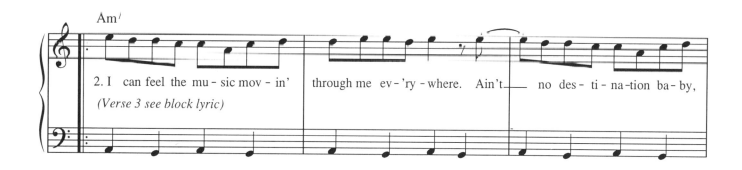

2. I can feel the mu - sic mov - in' through me ev - 'ry - where. Ain't___ no des - ti - na - tion ba - by,
(Verse 3 see block lyric)

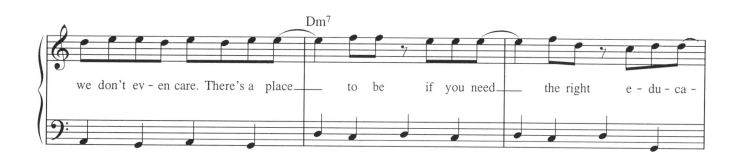

we don't ev - en care. There's a place___ to be if you need___ the right e - du - ca -

- tion. Let it take___ you there. (F) And just go___ with the ma - gic, ba - by.

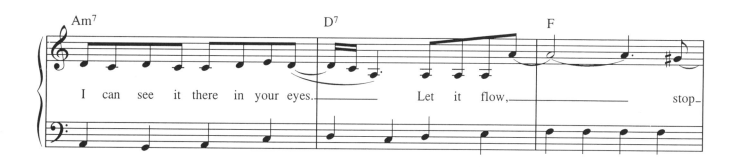

I can see it there in your eyes.___ Let it flow,___ stop_

the wait - ing, right here on the dance floor is where you got - ta let it go. Don't—

— stop mov - in', can— you feel the mu - sic? D.— J.'s got us go - in' a - round,—

— round.— Don't— stop mov - in', find— your own way to it. Lis -

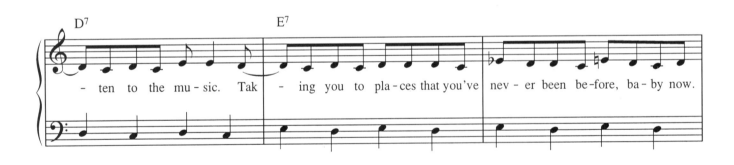

- ten to the mu - sic. Tak - ing you to pla - ces that you've nev - er been be - fore, ba - by now.

1.
Don't stop mov in' to the fun-ky, fun-ky beat. Don't stop mov in' to the fun-ky, fun-ky beat.

2. Am⁷

Don't stop mov-in' to the fun-ky, fun-ky beat. Don't stop mov-in' to the

Dm⁷

fun-ky, fun-ky beat. Yeah, oh come on! Don't stop mov-in' to the

Am⁷

fun-ky, fun-ky beat. Don't stop mov-in' to the fun-ky, fun-ky beat.

F   E⁷

For - get a - bout your fears_____ to - night,_____ lis -

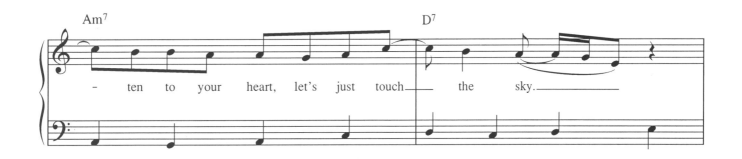

Am⁷   D⁷

- ten to your heart, let's just touch___ the sky._____

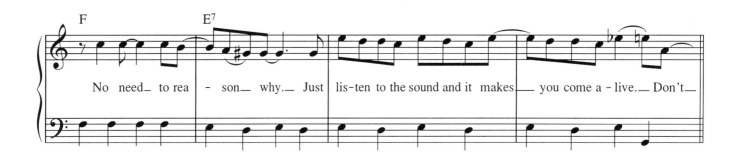

No need— to rea - son— why.— Just lis-ten to the sound and it makes— you come a - live.— Don't—

— stop mov - in', can— you feel the mu - sic? D.— J.'s got us go - in' a - round,—

— round.— Don't— stop mov - in', find— your own way to it. Lis -

1.
- ten to the mu - sic. Yeah,— yeah, yeah.— Don't— **2.** - ten to the mu - sic. Tak -

- ing you to pla - ces that you've nev - er been be - fore, ba - by now.

Don't stop mov-in' to the fun - ky, fun - ky beat. Don't stop mov-in' to the

fun - ky, fun - ky beat. Don't stop mov - in' to the

fun - ky, fun - ky beat. Don't stop mov - in' to the S Club beat.

Verse 3:

You can touch the moment almost feel it in the air
Don't know where we're goin' baby we don't even care
Ain't no mystery, just use your imagination
Let it take you there
Just go with your magic baby
I can see it there in your eyes
Let it flow, stop the waiting, right here on the dance floor
Is where you gotta let it go.

Don't stop movin' can you feel the music   *etc.*

Eternity

Words & Music by Robbie Williams & Guy Chambers

Moderately

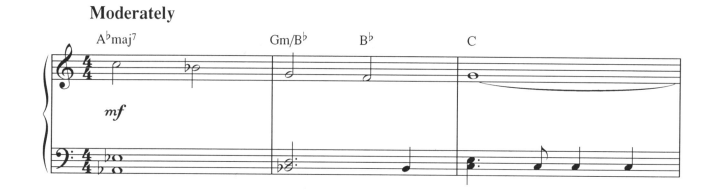

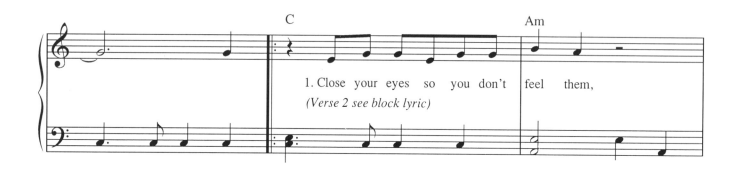

1. Close your eyes so you don't feel them,
(Verse 2 see block lyric)

they don't need to see you___ cry.___ I can pro-mise I will

heal you, but if you want___ I will try.___ I

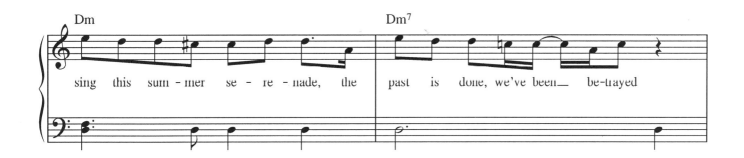

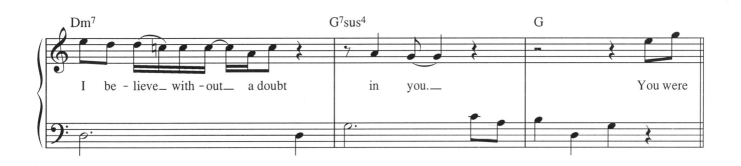

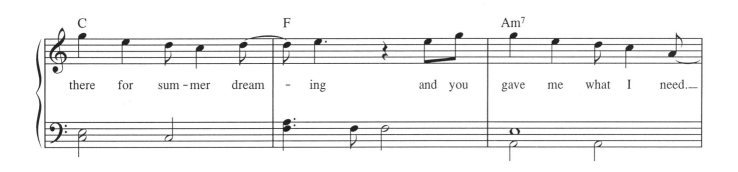

-ty._____ For e-ter - ni - ty.

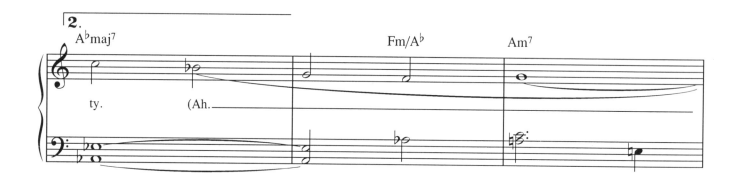

ty.   (Ah._____

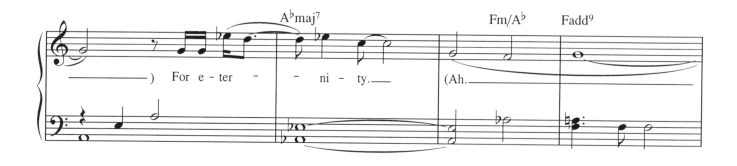

_____) For e-ter - - ni - ty.___ (Ah.

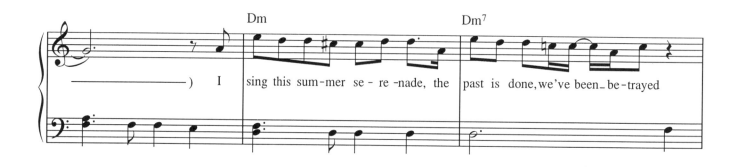

_____) I sing this sum-mer se-re-nade, the past is done, we've been be-trayed

it's true.— Youth is was-ted on the young be-

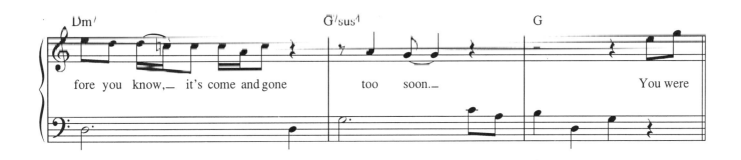

fore you know,— it's come and gone too soon.— You were

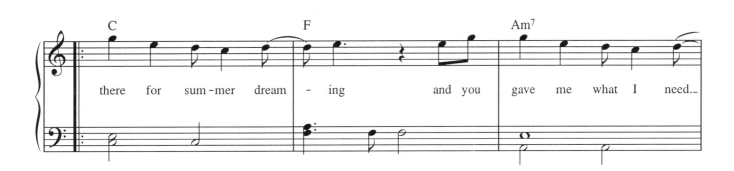

there for sum-mer dream — ing and you gave me what I need.—

_____ And I hope you'll find your free - dom___ for e - ter - ni -
2° (know)

ty.___ You were - dom___ e - ven - tual -

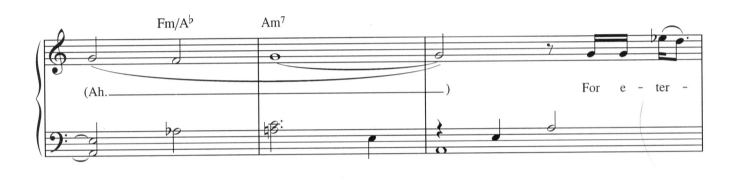

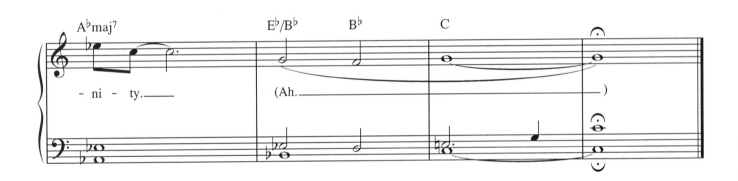

Verse 2:

Yesterday when you were walking
We talked about your Mum and Dad
What they did that made you happy
What they did that made you sad
We sat and watched the sun go down
Picked a star before we lost the moon
Youth is wasted on the young
Before you know, it's come and gone too soon.

You were there for summer dreaming   *etc.*

Have A Nice Day

Words & Music by Kelly Jones

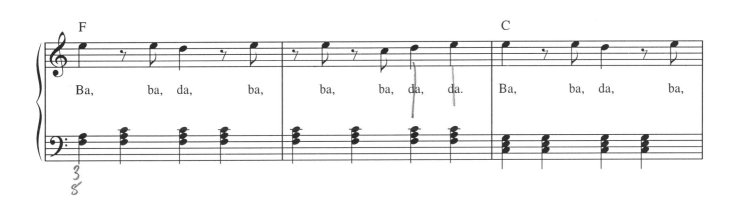

re-mem-ber what time.___ Got the wait-ing cab stopped at the red light,

ad-dress we're sure___ of but it's turned out just right.

2. It start-ed straight off: "com-ing here is hell." That's his first___ words,
3.   Lie around all day, have a drink to chase. Yourself and tour-ists, yeah
(Verse 4 see block lyric)

we asked what he meant.___ He said "Where ya from?" We told him our lot,
that's what I hate,___ He said "We're going wrong, we've all become the same,

"When ya take a ho - li - day
we dress the same— ways

Is this what you
only our ac - cents

want?"
change."

So have a nice—

day.—

have a nice—

day.—

have a nice—

day.—

have a nice—

To Coda ⊕ **1.**

day.—

2.

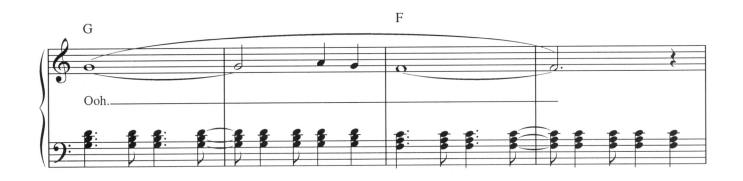

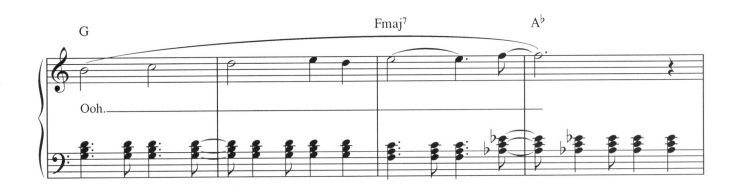

$\oplus$ *CODA*

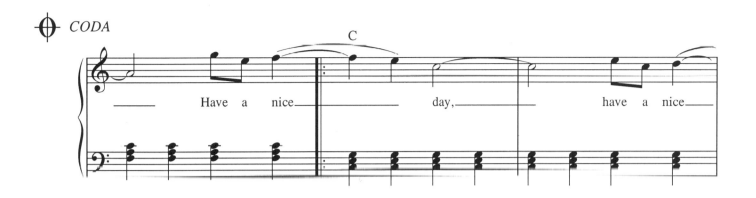

Have a nice day, have a nice

day, have a nice day,

Repeat to fade

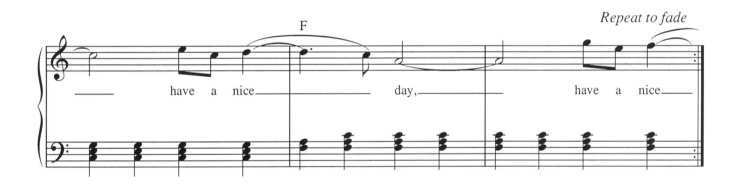

have a nice day, have a nice

Verse 4:

Swim in the ocean
That be my dish
I drive around all day
And kill processed fish.
It's all money gum
No artists anymore
You're only in it now
To make more, more, more.
So have a nice day *etc*.

Out Of Reach

Words & Music by Gabrielle & Jonathan Shorten

Moderately

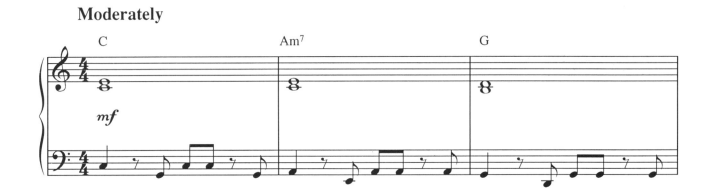

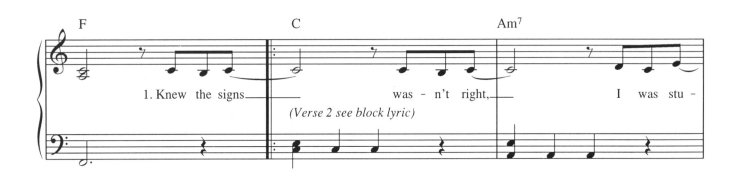

1. Knew the signs_____ was - n't right,_____ I was stu-

(Verse 2 see block lyric)

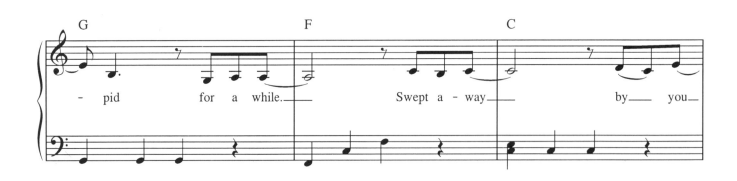

- pid for a while._____ Swept a - way_____ by___ you___

_____ and now I_____ feel like a fool.

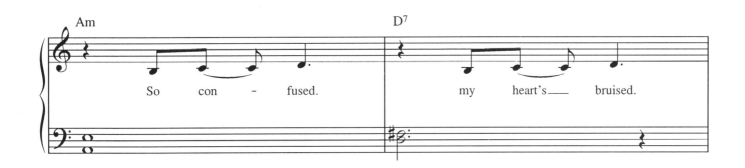

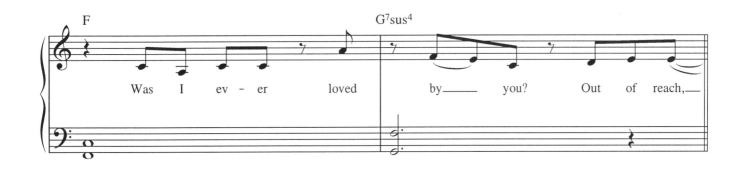

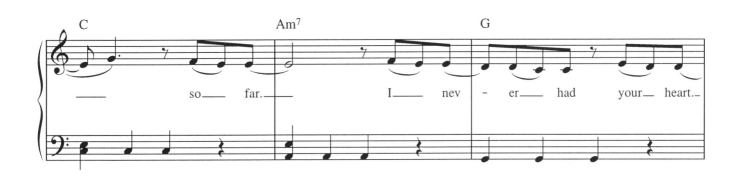

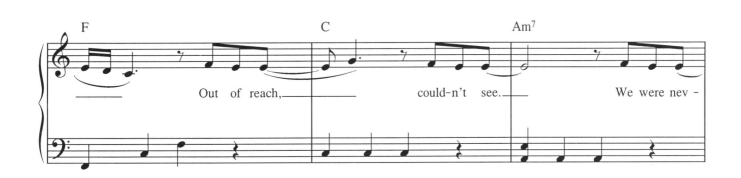

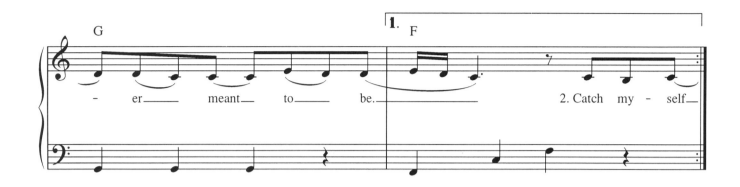

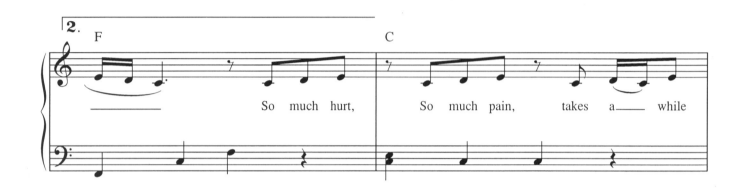

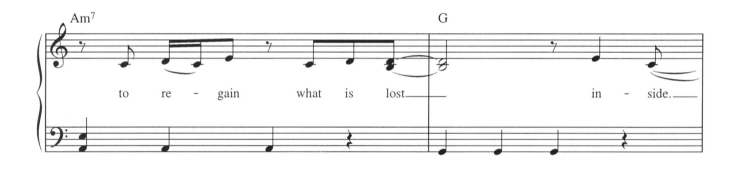

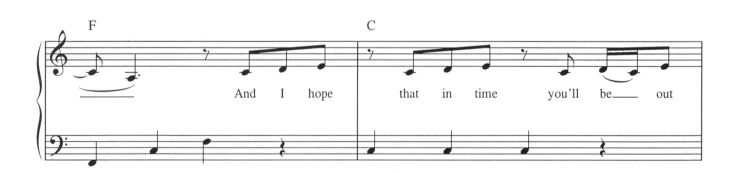

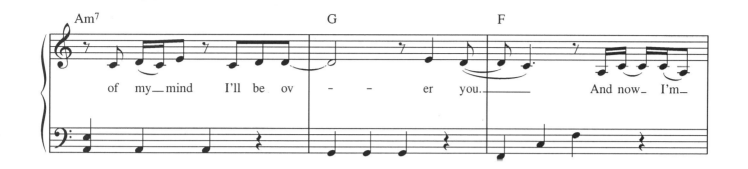

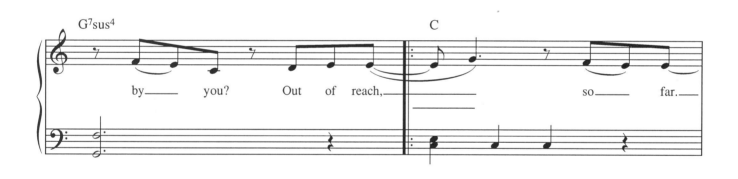

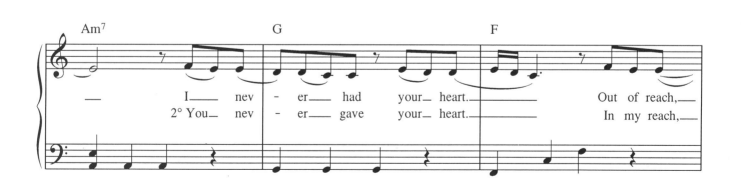

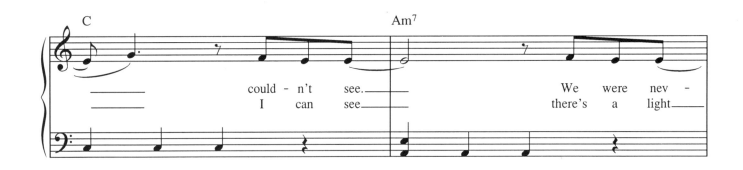

could - n't   see.
I   can   see

We   were   nev -
there's   a   light

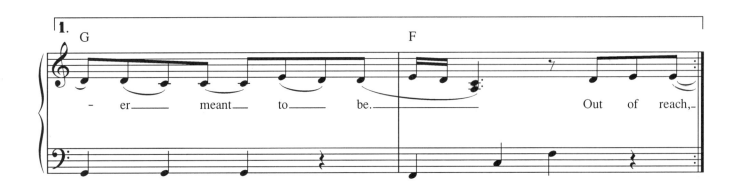

1.

- er   meant   to   be.

Out   of   reach,

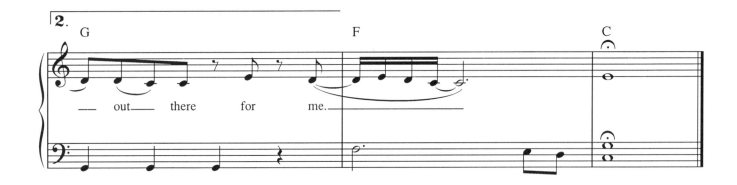

2.

out   there   for   me.

Verse 2:

Catch myself from despair
I could drown if I stay here
Keeping busy every day
I know I will be O.K.
But I was so confused
My heart's bruised
Was I ever loved by you?

Out of reach *etc*.

Pure And Simple

Words & Music by Tim Hawes, Pete Kirtley & Alison Clarkson

1. You been say-ing I'm driv-ing you cra-zy
(Verse 2 see block lyric)
and I have n't been a-round for you late-ly,

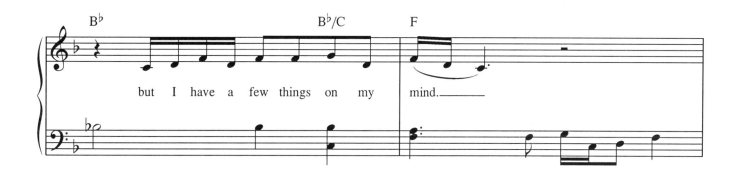

but I have a few things on my mind.

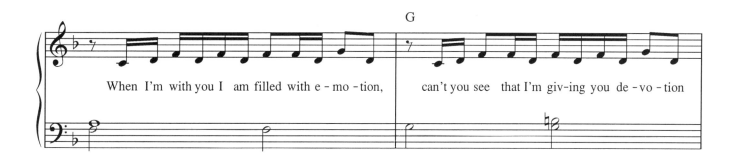

When I'm with you I am filled with e-mo-tion,
can't you see that I'm giv-ing you de-vo-tion

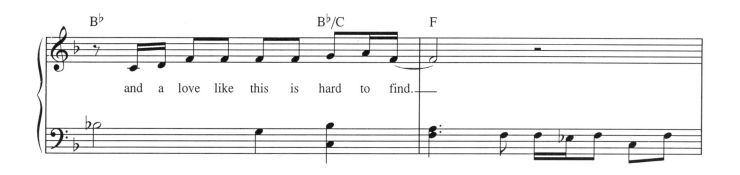

and a love like this is hard to find.

I know I've been a-walk-ing a-round in a daze.___ (Ba - by, ba - by.)

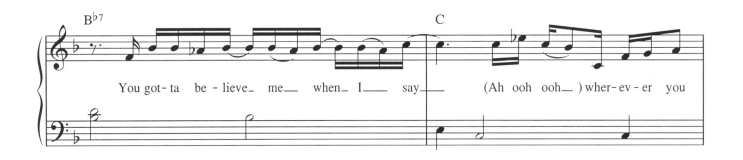

You got-ta be - lieve_ me_ when I___ say___ (Ah ooh ooh_) wher-ev-er you

go. (I'm gon-na be there) What ev-er you do, (You know I'm gon-na be there) it's pure and

sim-ple, (Oh yeah, yeah.) I'll be there_ for you. (Pure and sim-ple gon-na be there.) What-ev-er it

takes, (I'm gon-na be there) I swear it's true,___ (You know I'm gon-na be there) it's pure and

you're the on - ly one for me. (Yeah, yeah, yeah.___) (Ba - by, ba - by.)

(Ba - by, ba - by.) Wher - ev - er you

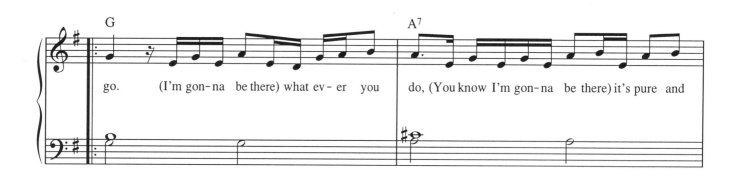

go. (I'm gon-na be there) what ev - er you do, (You know I'm gon-na be there) it's pure and

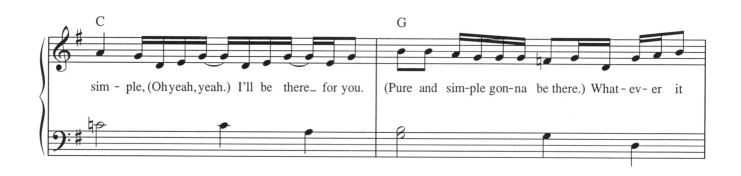

sim - ple, (Oh yeah, yeah.) I'll be there___ for you. (Pure and sim-ple gon-na be there.) What - ev - er it

takes,   (I'm gon-na be there) I swear it's   true,___ (You know I'm gon-na be there) it's pure and

sim - ple, (Oh yeah, yeah.) I'll be   there_ for you.   (Pure and sim - ple gon -na be there.) Wher-ev- er you

sim - ple, (Oh yeah, yeah.)_ I'll be   there_ for you.   (Pure and sim - ple gon -na be there.)

Verse 2:

I'll be there through the stormiest weather
Always trying to make things a bit better
And I know I gotta try and get through to you
You can love me in a way like no other
But the situation's taking you under
So you need to tell me now what you wanna do.

I know I've been walking around in daze (Baby, baby)
You gotta believe me when I say (Ah, ooh, ooh)

Wherever you go *etc.*

This Year's Love

Words & Music by David Gray

And when you hold me like you do it feels_ so_ right,_ oh now,_

I start to for-get how my heart gets torn when that
(Verse 3 see block lyric)

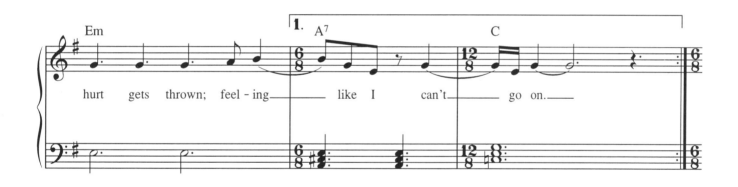

hurt gets thrown; feel-ing_ like I can't_ go on._

dream in-side my soul, when you kiss me on that mid-night street, sweep me

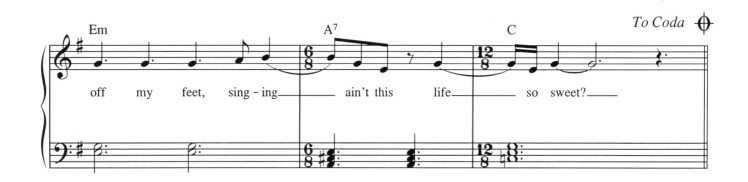

off my feet, sing - ing_____ ain't this life_____ so sweet?_____

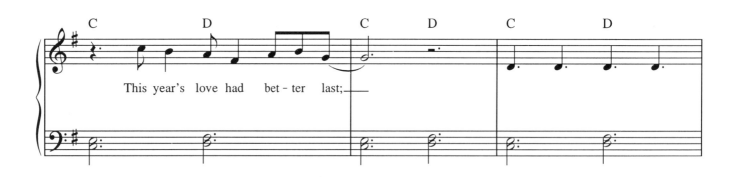

This year's love had bet - ter last;_____

D.S. al Coda
(As 2°)

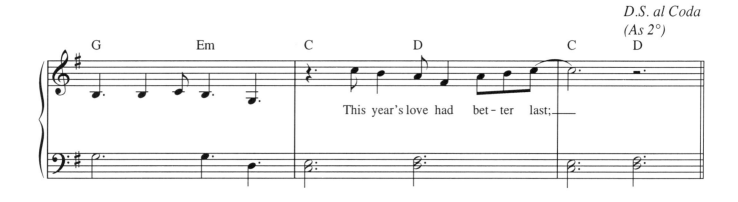

This year's love had bet - ter last;_____

⊕ *CODA*

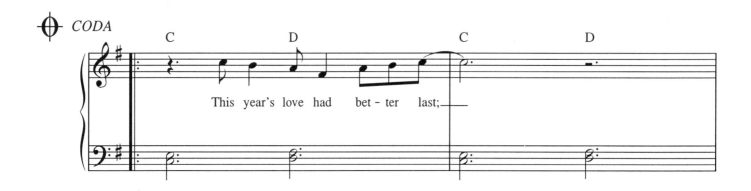

This year's love had bet - ter last;_____

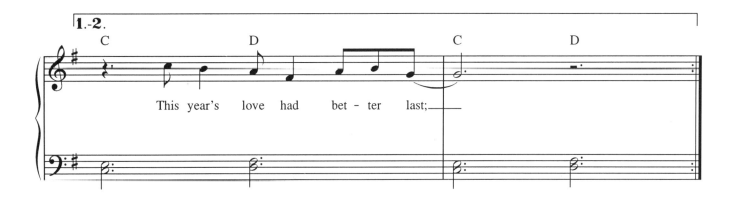

1.-2.

This year's love had bet - ter last;

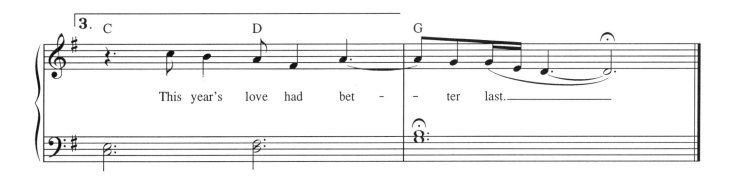

3.

This year's love had bet - - ter last.

Verse 2:

Turning circles and time again
It cuts like a knife, oh now
If you love me I got to know for sure
'Cause it takes something more this time
Than sweet, sweet lies, oh now
Before I open up my arms and fall
Losing all control
Every dream inside my soul
When you kiss me on that midnight street
Sweep me off my feet
Singing ain't this life so sweet.

Verse 3:

'Cause who's to worry if our hearts get torn
When that hurt gets thrown?
Don't you know this life goes on?
Won't you kiss me on that midnight street
Sweep me off my feet
Singing ain't this life so sweet?

What Took You So Long?

Words & Music by Emma Bunton, Richard Stannard, Julian Gallagher, Martin Harrington, John Themis & Dave Morgan

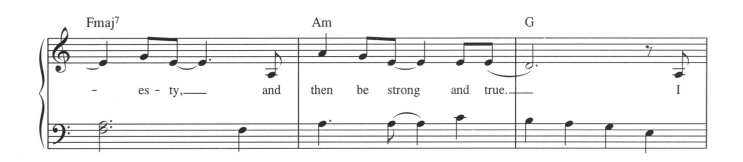

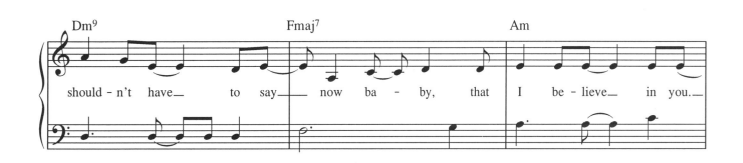

night? What took you for - ev - er to see___ I'm right? You know I treat you so

good, I make you feel fine. You know I'll nev - er give it up this time.___

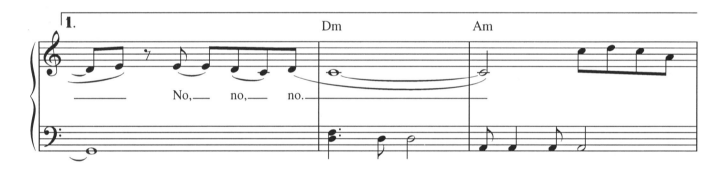

___ No,___ no,___ no.___

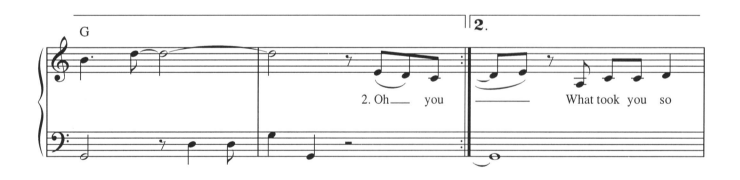

2. Oh___ you ___ What took you so

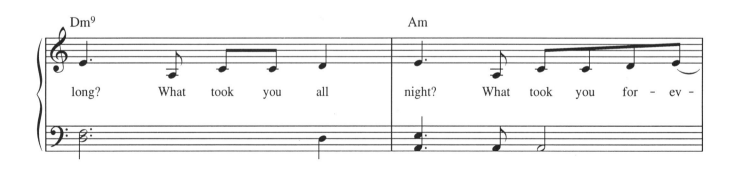

long? What took you all night? What took you for - ev -

-er to see___ I'm right? You know I treat you so good, I make you feel

fine. You know I'll nev - er give it up this time.___ No,___ no,___ no.

No,___ no,___ no. Oh,___

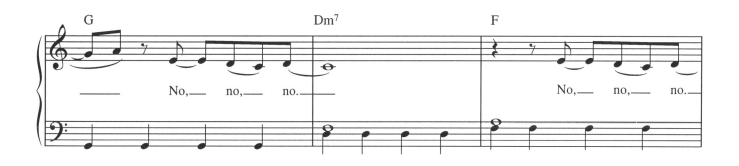

___ No,___ no,___ no.

Oh.___ Ba - by,

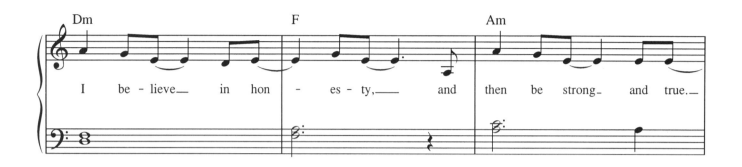

- er to see— I'm right? You know I treat you so good, I make you feel

fine. You know I'll nev - er give it up this time.— No,— no,— no.—

Verse 2:

Oh, you touched my heart right from the start
You didn't know what to say
But honey understand when you take my hand
Everything's okay
'Cause baby I believe reality
Is never far away
I've had enough, so listen baby
I've got something to say.

What took you so long *etc.*

Whole Again

Words & Music by Stuart Kershaw, Andy McCluskey, Bill Padley & Jeremy Godfrey

Moderately

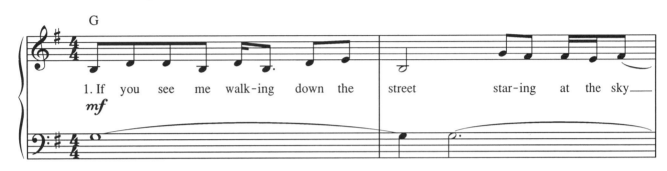

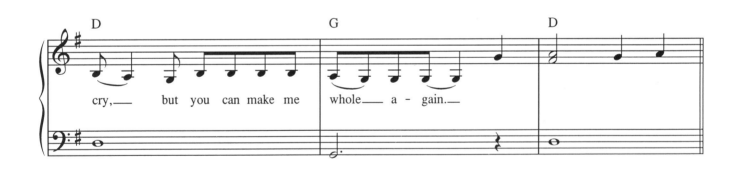

- king, do-ing what I can, I won't put you down, 'cause I want you a-

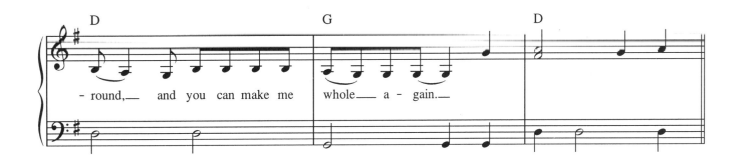

- round,___ and you can make me whole___ a - gain.___

Look - in' back on where we first met, I___ can - not es -

- cape___ and I can-not for - get.___ Ba - by you're the one, you___ still turn me

on,___ you can make me whole___ a - gain.___

For now I'll have to wait, but ba - by if you change your

mind, don't be too late 'cause I just can't go on, it's al - rea - dy been too

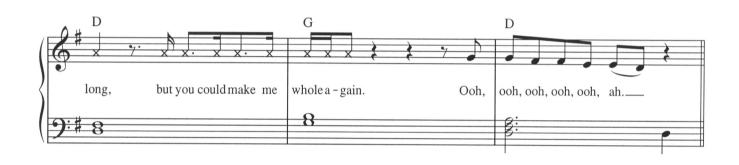

long, but you could make me whole a - gain. Ooh, ooh, ooh, ooh, ooh, ah.

Look - in' back on where we first met, I can - not es -

- cape and I can - not for - get. Ba - by you're the

one,   you___ still turn me   on,___   you can make me   whole___ a - gain.___

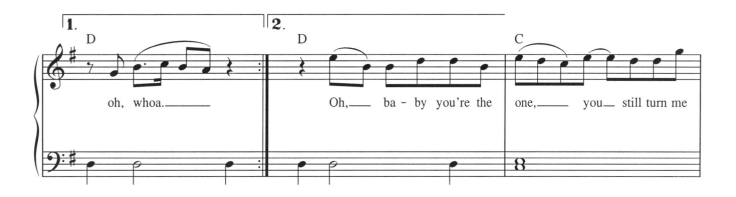

oh, whoa.___   Oh,___ ba - by you're the   one,___   you___ still turn me

on,___   you   can   make   me   whole___ a - gain.___

Verse 2:

Time is laying heavy on my heart
Seems I've got too much of it since we've been apart
My friends make me smile, if only for a while
You can make me whole again.

Sing

Words & Music by Fran Healy

Moderately

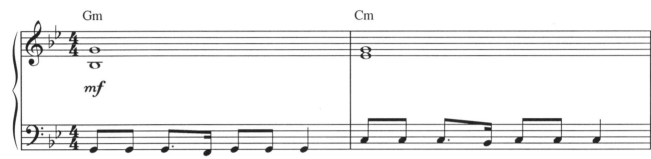

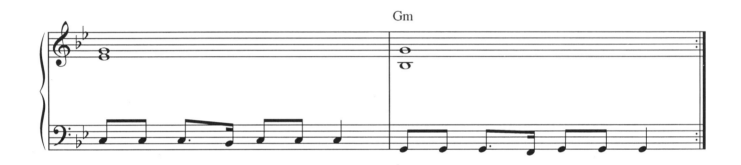

1. Ba - by, you've been go - in' so cra - zy, late -

(Verse 2 see block lyric)

- ly no - thin' seems to be go - in' right. So

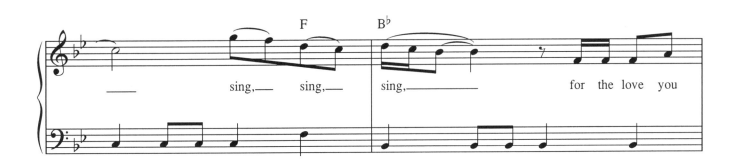

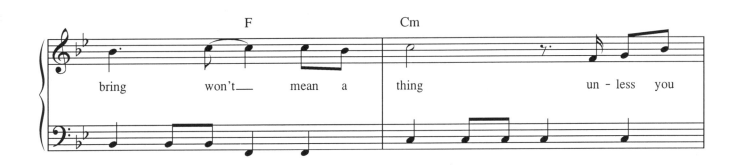

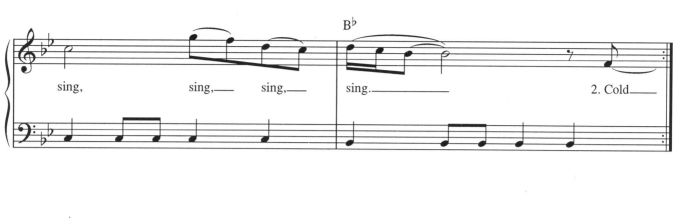

sing, sing,— sing,— sing.— 2. Cold—

Ooh.—

— Oh,— oh,— oh.—

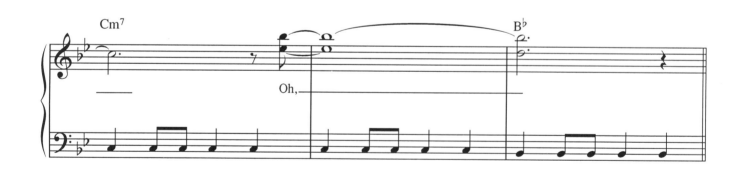

— Oh,—

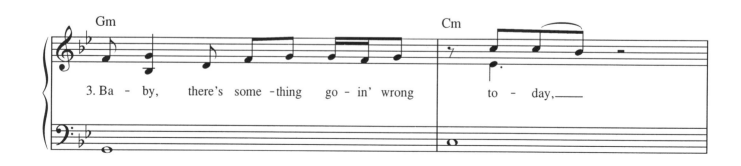

3. Ba - by, there's some-thing go-in' wrong to - day,—

but I say no-thing, no-thing, no-thing, no-thing, no-thing,

no-thing, no-thing, no-thing, no-thing, no-thing. So na, na, na, na, now if you sing,

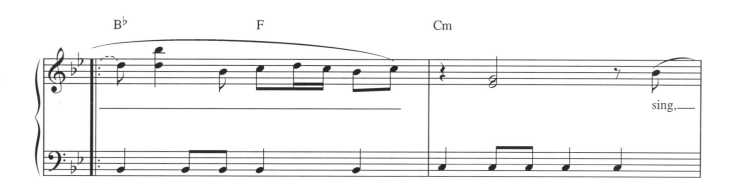

sing,

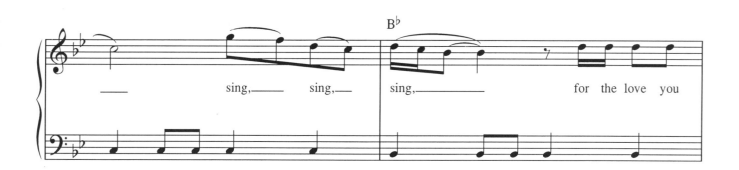

sing, sing, sing, for the love you

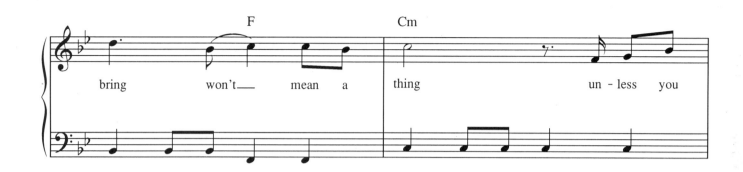

bring won't___ mean a thing un-less you

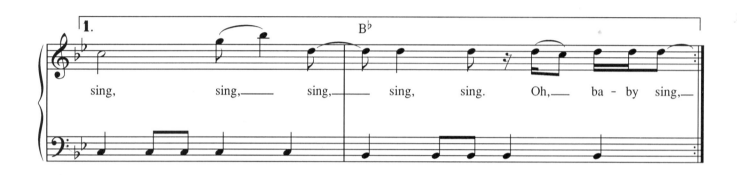

1. sing, sing,___ sing,___ sing, sing. Oh,___ ba-by sing,___

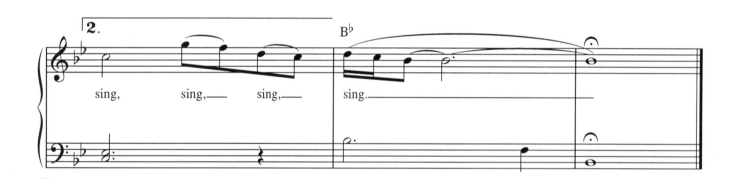

2. sing, sing,___ sing,___ sing.___

Verse 2:

Colder, crying over your shoulder
Hold her, tell her everything's gonna be fine
Surely you've been going to hurry
Hurry, 'cause no-one's gonna be stopped.

Not if you sing *etc.*